High Fibre

Recipes and Practical Advice for your Health

General Editor: Gina Steer

FLAME TREE
PUBLISHING

Publisher & Creative Director: Nick Wells
Project Editor: Sarah Goulding
Designer: Mike Spender
With thanks to: Gina Steer

This is a **FLAME TREE** Book

FLAME TREE PUBLISHING
Crabtree Hall, Crabtree Lane
Fulham, London SW6 6TY
United Kingdom
www.flametreepublishing.com

Flame Tree is part of The Foundry Creative Media Company Limited

First published 2005

05 07 09 08 06
1 3 5 7 9 10 8 6 4 2

ISBN 1 84451 113 8

A copy of the CIP data for this book is available from the British Library.

Printed in Malaysia

Contents

Enjoying a High Fibre Lifestyle

Many believe the saying 'you are what you eat', and whether this is true or not there is no denying that a healthy lifestyle is vital for us all. A healthy lifestyle embraces diet (both food and drink) and exercise, two things that are essential for everyone, no matter what age group they belong to. Food and drink are required for survival and contain our bodies' building blocks. It follows that the healthier your diet, the better your quality of life, and in many cases the longer your life will be. It therefore makes sense that you look at your diet, and change or amend it if necessary.

Most diets tend to be high in refined foods such as white bread, white flour and processed cereals, from which natural fibre has been stripped. A diet low in fibre may lead to constipation or bowel disorders, but by increasing the amount of fibre you eat you may help to prevent these problems. A high fibre diet is therefore not a 'special' diet or one to be embarked on only on medical advice, but a way of life for anyone wanting to be healthy. Fibre provides the fuel for our bodies that keeps us going, giving us the energy not only to move around, exercise and work but also to repair the body and grow. Deprived of this, the body will quickly start to break down.

Recently there have been a rush of popular diets, many of which have advocated reducing or eliminating carbohydrates, the source of all dietary fibre. This is a very dangerous way of eating. If the diet concentrates more on protein and fats there is the danger that, over time, vital organs begin to break down and life-threatening illness can occur. Fibre is vital to ensure the smooth running of the digestive system. It therefore cannot be stated too strongly that a well-balanced diet is essential for good health. As a general rule, the British Department of Health advocates that half the total intake of food should be carbohydrate and the other half made up of protein and fats. Unfortunately the reverse is true for many of us, which is when problems can start to occur. It is interesting to note that other countries advocate a different breakdown and recommend an even higher proportion of carbohydrate to fat and protein – the World Health Organisation, for instance, advocates a carbohydrate/fibre intake of between 55–75 per cent.

Energy consumed by us is calculated in kilo calories (often shortened to calories) and a certain recommended daily intake is advised by health experts, although it should be noted that the actual amount required by each individual depends on age, activity, the ratio of fat to muscle, and other factors such as being overweight, ill or fighting a disease. For people maintaining a reasonably active lifestyle the guidelines are as follows:

Men (aged 19–59) 2,550 kcal

Women (aged 19–50) 1,940 kcal or (aged 51–59) 1,990

When trying to lose weight it is the fat that should be drastically reduced, then the protein. The carbohydrate (especially in the form of fibre) should if anything be increased, but unfortunately it is the carbohydrate that is normally reduced. Most foods, with the exception of oils and sugar, are a mixture of fibre, fats and protein in a lesser or greater degree. It is therefore important that there is a greater understanding of what components are contained within the foods so that an informed decision can be made.

There are two main kinds of carbohydrates – starch and sugar. Starch carbohydrates are also known as complex carbohydrates and they include cereals, pulses, beans, breads, potatoes, pasta and rice. Eating wholegrain varieties of these foods will provide you with plenty of fibre. Sugar carbohydrates, or intrinsic sugars, are found in fruits and vegetables. These are 'good' sugars, as they still contain their cellular structure which, again, provides us with fibre. The extrinsic sugars, as found in sugar, honey, fruit squashes, cakes, biscuits and sweets, etc. are bad for us as they are refined, with all of the cellular structure removed. As a general guide, you should try to eat more of the following: wholemeal bread and pasta, brown rice, wholemeal flour to make pastry or homemade cakes and biscuits, wholegrain breakfast cereals, plenty of vegetables and fruit (especially oranges, pears, apples, avocados, grapefruits, prunes, berries, figs, pulses including baked beans, kidney beans and lentils, jacket potatoes, carrots, sweetcorn, broad beans, runner beans, peas and sprouts) and nuts such as peanuts, almonds and coconut. Always remember to drink plenty of fluids on a high fibre diet, as fibre retains fluid and you may become dehydrated easily.

Complex carbohydrates are a good choice for those concerned about weight gain as they are bulky and slow to digest, so will keep you feeling fuller for longer and reduce the desire to snack. These also contain minerals and vitamins and help the body conserve the benefits of any protein consumed. A further advantage is that, by eating a lot of fibre, the fat content of the diet is very much reduced and cholesterol levels are kept low. Eating high amounts of fat, especially saturated fat, has been proven to increase blocking of the arteries and lead to heart problems such as angina, strokes and heart attacks.

The best sources of fibre in our diet come from complex carbohydrates and come in two forms, soluble and insoluble. Insoluble fibre comes mainly from plants, and good sources are wheat, corn, rice, pulses and vegetables. The importance of insoluble fibre in the diet is paramount, as it helps to keep the intestines healthy and the digestive system in good working order. Fibre helps to prevent constipation and is believed to help in the prevention of bowel cancer. Soluble fibre is found in fruits, barley and rye and many believe that a good supply of soluble fibre helps to prevent LDL – the bad cholesterol found in blood.

It is generally recommended that 24 g per day of fibre is consumed to maintain a healthy diet, although it is estimated that in the west we consume only 13 g per day. Eating more will have untold benefits on your health.

This book has been especially designed to help you increase the amount of fibre in your diet, whether you are doing it on medical advice or just because you want to eat more healthily. The recipes are delicious, easy to prepare and cook, and offer a broad span of tasty recipes that will appeal to all. From Brown Rice Spiced Pilaf and Cream of Pumpkin Soup to Potato Skins and Crunchy Rhubarb Crumble, you'll find something everyone will love whether they're following a high fibre diet or not.

Aduki Bean & Rice Burgers

Nutritional details

per 100 g

energy	104 kcals/436 kj
protein	5 g
carbohydrate	15 g
fat	3 g
fibre	2.2 g
sugar	2.7 g
sodium	0.2 g

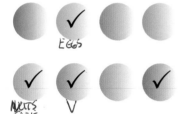

EGGS

NUTS FREE   V

Ingredients   Serves 4

2½ tbsp sunflower oil
1 medium onion, peeled
    and very finely chopped
1 garlic clove, peeled and crushed
1 tsp curry paste
225 g/8 oz basmati rice
400 g can aduki beans,
    drained and rinsed
225 ml/8 fl oz vegetable stock
125 g/4 oz firm tofu, crumbled
1 tsp garam masala
2 tbsp freshly chopped coriander
salt and freshly ground
    black pepper

For the carrot raita:
2 large carrots, peeled and grated
½ cucumber, cut into tiny cubes
150 ml/¼ pint Greek yogurt

To serve:
wholemeal baps
tomato slices
lettuce leaves

Step-by-step guide

1   Heat 1 tablespoon of the oil in a saucepan and gently cook the onion for 10 minutes until soft. Add the garlic and curry paste and cook for a few more seconds. Stir in the rice and beans.

2   Pour in the stock, bring to the boil and simmer for 12 minutes, or until all the stock has been absorbed – do not lift the lid for the first 10 minutes of cooking. Reserve.

3   Lightly mash the tofu. Add to the rice mixture with the garam masala, coriander, salt and pepper. Mix.

4   Divide the mixture into eight and shape into burgers. Chill in the refrigerator for 30 minutes.

5   Meanwhile, make the raita. Mix together the carrots, cucumber and Greek yogurt. Spoon into a small bowl and chill in the refrigerator until ready to serve.

6   Heat the remaining oil in a large frying pan. Fry the burgers, in batches if necessary, for 4–5 minutes on each side, or until lightly browned. Serve in the baps with tomato slices and lettuce. Accompany with the raita.

✓ cows' milk-free   ✓ egg-free   ✓ gluten-free   ✓ wheat-free   ✓ nut-free   ✓ vegetarian   ✓ vegan   ✓ seafood-free

Beef & Baby Corn Stir Fry

Nutritional details

per 100 g

energy	102 kcals/427 kj
protein	9 g
carbohydrate	7 g
fat	4 g
fibre	1.2 g
sugar	1.8 g
sodium	0.3 g

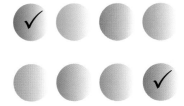

Ingredients   Serves 4

3 tbsp light soy sauce
1 tbsp clear honey, warmed
450 g/1 lb beef rump steak, trimmed
    and thinly sliced
6 tbsp groundnut oil
125 g/4 oz shiitake mushrooms,
    wiped and halved
125 g/4 oz beansprouts, rinsed
2.5 cm/1 inch piece fresh root ginger,
    peeled and cut into matchsticks
125 g/4 oz mangetout,
    halved lengthways
125 g/4 oz broccoli,
    trimmed and cut into florets
1 medium carrot,
    peeled and cut into matchsticks
125 g/4 oz baby sweetcorn cobs,
    halved lengthways
¼ head Chinese leaves, shredded
1 tbsp chilli sauce
3 tbsp black bean sauce
1 tbsp dry sherry
freshly cooked noodles,
    to serve

Step-by-step guide

1   Mix together the soy sauce and honey in a shallow dish. Add the sliced beef and turn to coat evenly. Cover with clingfilm and leave to marinate for at least 30 minutes, turning occasionally.

2   Heat a wok or large frying pan, add 2 tablespoons of the oil and heat until just smoking. Add the mushrooms and stir-fry for 1 minute. Add the bean sprouts and stir-fry for 1 minute. Using a slotted spoon, transfer the mushroom mixture to a plate and keep warm.

3   Drain the beef, reserving the marinade. Reheat the wok, pour in 2 tablespoons of the oil and heat until smoking. Add the beef and stir-fry for 4 minutes or until browned. Transfer to a plate and keep warm.

4   Add the remaining oil to the wok and heat until just smoking. Add the ginger, mangetout, broccoli, carrot and the baby sweetcorn with the shredded Chinese leaves and stir-fry for 3 minutes. Stir in the chilli and black bean sauces, the sherry, the reserved marinade and the beef and mushroom mixture. Stir-fry for 2 minutes, then serve immediately with freshly cooked noodles.

✓ cows' milk-free   ✓ egg-free   ✓ gluten-free   ✓ wheat-free   ✓ nut-free   ✓ vegetarian   ✓ vegan   ✓ seafood-free

Black Bean Chilli with Avocado Salsa

Nutritional details

per 100 g

energy	117 kcals/491 kj
protein	5 g
carbohydrate	16 g
fat	4 g
fibre	2.2 g
sugar	3.4 g
sodium	0.2 g

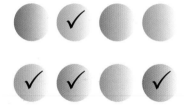

Ingredients   Serves 4

250 g/9 oz dried black beans and
    black-eye beans, soaked overnight
2 tbsp olive oil
1 large onion, peeled
    and finely chopped
1 red pepper, deseeded and diced
2 garlic cloves,
    peeled and finely chopped
1 red chilli, deseeded
    and finely chopped
2 tsp chilli powder
1 tsp ground cumin
2 tsp ground coriander
400 g can chopped tomatoes
450 ml/¾ pint vegetable stock
1 small ripe avocado, diced
½ small red onion,
    peeled and finely chopped
2 tbsp freshly chopped coriander
juice of 1 lime
1 small tomato, peeled,
    deseeded and diced
salt and freshly ground black pepper
25 g/1 oz dark chocolate

To garnish:
half-fat crème fraîche
lime slices
sprigs of coriander

Step-by-step guide

1   Drain the beans and place in a large saucepan with at least twice their volume of fresh water.

2   Bring slowly to the boil, skimming off any froth that rises to the surface. Boil rapidly for 10 minutes, then reduce the heat and simmer for about 45 minutes, adding more water if necessary. Drain and reserve.

3   Heat the oil in a large saucepan and add the onion and pepper. Cook for 3–4 minutes until softened. Add the garlic and chilli.

Cook for 5 minutes, or until the onion and pepper have softened. Add the chilli powder, cumin and coriander and cook for 30 seconds. Add the beans along with the tomatoes and stock.

4   Bring to the boil and simmer uncovered for 40–45 minutes until the beans and vegetables are tender and the sauce has reduced.

5   Mix together the avocado, onion, fresh coriander, lime juice and tomato. Season with salt and pepper and set aside. Remove the chilli from the heat. Break the chocolate into pieces and sprinkle over the chilli. Leave for 2 minutes, then stir well. Garnish with crème fraîche, lime and coriander and serve with the avocado salsa.

✓ cows' milk-free   ✓ egg-free   ✓ gluten-free   ✓ wheat-free   ✓ nut-free   ✓ vegetarian   ✓ vegan   ✓ seafood-free

Boston-style Baked Beans

Nutritional details

per 100 g

energy	228 kcals/960 kj
protein	9 g
carbohydrate	45 g
fat	2 g
fibre	1.1 g
sugar	14 g
sodium	0.2 g

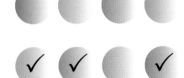

Ingredients   Serves 8

350 g/12 oz mixed dried
    pulses, e.g. haricot,
    flageolet, cannellini,
    and pinto beans or chickpeas
1 large onion, peeled and
    finely chopped
125 g/4 oz black treacle
    or molasses
2 tbsp Dijon mustard
2 tbsp light brown soft sugar
125 g/4 oz plain flour
150 g/5 oz fine cornmeal
2 tbsp caster sugar
2½ tsp baking powder
½ tsp salt
2 tbsp freshly chopped thyme
2 medium eggs
200 ml/7 fl oz milk
2 tbsp melted butter
salt and freshly ground
    black pepper
parsley sprigs, to garnish

Step-by-step guide

1 Preheat the oven to 130°C/250°F/ Gas Mark ½. Put the pulses into a large saucepan and cover with at least twice their volume of water. Bring to the boil and simmer for 2 minutes. Leave to stand for 1 hour. Return to the boil and boil rapidly for about 10 minutes. Drain and reserve.

2 Mix together the onion, treacle or molasses, mustard and sugar in a large mixing bowl. Add the drained beans and 300 ml/½ pint fresh water. Stir well, bring to the boil, cover and transfer to the preheated oven for 4 hours in an ovenproof dish, stirring once every hour and adding more water if necessary.

3 When the beans are cooked, remove from the oven and keep warm. Increase the oven temperature to 200°C/400°F/ Gas Mark 6. Mix together the plain flour, cornmeal, caster sugar, baking powder, salt and most of the thyme, reserving about one third for garnish. In a separate bowl beat the eggs, then stir in the milk and butter. Pour the wet ingredients on to the dry ones and stir just enough to combine.

4 Pour into a buttered 18 cm/7 inch square cake tin. Sprinkle over the remaining thyme. Bake for 30 minutes until golden and risen or until a toothpick inserted into the centre comes out clean. Cut into squares, then reheat the beans. Season to taste with salt and pepper and serve immediately, garnished with parsley sprigs and thyme.

cows' milk-free ✓ egg-free ✓ gluten-free ✓ wheat-free ✓ nut-free ✓ vegetarian ✓ vegan ✓ seafood-free

Braised Chicken with Aubergine

Nutritional details

per 100 g

energy	80 kcals/337 kj
protein	7 g
carbohydrate	7 g
fat	3 g
fibre	1 g
sugar	0.2 g
sodium	0.2 g

Ingredients   Serves 4

3 tbsp vegetable oil
12 chicken thighs
2 large aubergines,
   trimmed and cubed
4 garlic cloves,
   peeled and crushed
2 tsp freshly grated
   root ginger
900 ml/1½ pints vegetable stock
2 tbsp light soy sauce
2 tbsp Chinese preserved
   black beans
6 spring onions, trimmed and
   thinly sliced diagonally
1 tbsp cornflour
1 tbsp sesame oil
spring onion tassels,
   to garnish
freshly cooked noodles or rice,
   to serve

Step-by-step guide

1   Heat a wok or large frying pan, add the oil and when hot, add the chicken thighs and cook over a medium high heat for 5 minutes, or until browned all over. Transfer to a large plate and keep warm.

2   Add the aubergine to the wok and cook over a high heat for 5 minutes or until browned, turning occasionally. Add the garlic and ginger and stir-fry for 1 minute.

3   Return the chicken to the wok, pour in the stock and add the soy sauce and black beans. Bring to the boil, then simmer for 20 minutes, or until the chicken is tender. Add the spring onions after 10 minutes.

4   Blend the cornflour with 2 tablespoons of water. Stir into the wok and simmer until the sauce has thickened. Stir in the sesame oil, heat for 30 seconds, then remove from the heat. Garnish with spring onion tassels and serve immediately with noodles or rice.

✓ cows' milk-free   ✓ egg-free   ✓ gluten-free   ✓ wheat-free   ✓ nut-free   ✓ vegetarian   ✓ vegan   ✓ seafood-free

Braised Lamb with Broad Beans

Nutritional details

per 100 g

energy	154 kcals/645 kj
protein	13 g
carbohydrate	6 g
fat	9 g
fibre	1.1 g
sugar	1.4 g
sodium	0.1 g

Ingredients   Serves 4

700 g/1½ lb lamb,
    cut into large chunks
1 tbsp plain flour
1 onion
2 garlic cloves
1 tbsp olive oil
400 g can chopped tomatoes
    with basil
300 ml/½ pint lamb stock
2 tbsp freshly chopped thyme
2 tbsp freshly chopped oregano
salt and freshly ground black pepper
150 g/5 oz frozen broad beans
fresh oregano, to garnish
creamy mashed potatoes,
    to serve

Step-by-step guide

1 Trim the lamb, discarding any fat or gristle, then place the flour in a polythene bag, add the lamb and toss until coated thoroughly. Peel and slice the onion and garlic and reserve. Heat the olive oil in a heavy-based saucepan and when hot, add the lamb and cook, stirring until the meat is sealed and browned all over. Using a slotted spoon, transfer the lamb to a plate and reserve.

2 Add the onion and garlic to the saucepan and cook for 3 minutes, stirring frequently until softened, then return the lamb to the saucepan. Add the chopped tomatoes with their juice, the stock, the chopped thyme and oregano to the pan and season to taste with salt and pepper. Bring to the boil, then cover with a close-fitting lid, reduce the heat and simmer for 1 hour.

3 Add the broad beans to the lamb and simmer for 20–30 minutes, or until the lamb is tender. Garnish with fresh oregano and serve with creamy mashed potatoes.

Broad Bean & Artichoke Risotto

Nutritional details

per 100 g

energy	99 kcals/412 kj
protein	5 g
carbohydrate	11 g
fat	4 g
fibre	1.4 g
sugar	0.9 g
sodium	0.4 g

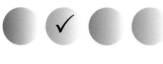

Ingredients   Serves 4

275 g/10 oz frozen broad beans
400 g can artichoke hearts, drained
1 tbsp sunflower oil
150 ml/¼ pint dry white wine
900 ml/1½ pints vegetable stock
25 g/1 oz butter
1 onion, peeled and finely chopped
200 g/7 oz Arborio rice
finely grated rind and juice of 1 lemon
50 g/2 oz Parmesan cheese, grated
salt and freshly ground black pepper
freshly grated Parmesan cheese,
    to serve

Step-by-step guide

1   Cook the beans in a saucepan
    of lightly salted boiling water for
    4–5 minutes, or until just tender.
    Drain and plunge into cold water.
    Peel off the tough outer skins, if
    liked. Pat the artichokes dry on
    absorbent kitchen paper and cut
    each in half lengthways through
    the stem end. Cut each half into
    three wedges.

2   Heat the oil in a large saucepan
    and cook the artichokes for
    4–5 minutes, turning occasionally,
    until they are lightly browned.
    Remove and reserve. Bring the
    wine and stock to the boil in a
    separate frying pan. Keep them
    barely simmering while making
    the risotto.

3   Melt the butter in a large frying
    pan, add the onion and cook for
    5 minutes until beginning to
    soften. Add the rice and cook
    for 1 minute, stirring. Pour in a
    ladleful of the hot wine and stock
    and simmer gently, stirring, until
    the stock is absorbed. Continue
    to add the stock in this way for
    20–25 minutes, until the rice is
    just tender; the risotto should
    look creamy and soft.

4   Add the broad beans, artichokes,
    and lemon rind and juice. Gently
    mix in, cover and leave to warm
    through for 1–2 minutes. Stir in
    the Parmesan cheese and season
    to taste with salt and pepper.
    Serve sprinkled with extra
    Parmesan cheese.

✓ cows' milk-free   ✓ egg-free   ✓ gluten-free   ✓ wheat-free   ✓ nut-free   ✓ vegetarian   ✓ vegan   ✓ seafood-free

Brown Rice & Lentil Salad with Duck

Nutritional details

per 100 g

energy	177 kcals/734 kj
protein	10 g
carbohydrate	9 g
fat	12 g
fibre	1 g
sugar	1.2 g
sodium	0.3 g

Ingredients   Serves 6

225 g/8 oz Puy lentils, rinsed
4 tbsp olive oil
1 medium onion,
   peeled and finely chopped
200 g/7 oz long-grain brown rice
½ tsp dried thyme
450 ml/¾ pint chicken stock
salt and freshly ground
   black pepper
350 g/12 oz shiitake or portabella
   mushrooms, trimmed and sliced
375 g/13 oz cooked Chinese-style
   spicy duck or roasted duck,
   sliced into chunks
2 garlic cloves, peeled and
   finely chopped
125 g/4 oz cooked smoked
   ham, diced
2 small courgettes, trimmed,
   diced and blanched
6 spring onions, trimmed and
   thinly sliced
2 tbsp freshly chopped parsley
2 tbsp walnut halves,
   toasted and chopped

For the dressing:

2 tbsp red or white wine vinegar
1 tbsp balsamic vinegar
1 tsp Dijon mustard
1 tsp clear honey
75 ml/3 fl oz extra virgin olive oil
2–3 tbsp walnut oil

Step-by-step guide

1   Bring a large saucepan of water to the boil, sprinkle in the lentils, return to the boil, then simmer over a low heat for 30 minutes, or until tender; do not overcook. Drain and rinse under cold running water, then drain again and reserve.

2   Heat 2 tablespoons of the oil in a saucepan. Add the onion and cook for 2 minutes until it begins to soften. Stir in the rice with the thyme and stock. Season to taste with salt and pepper and bring to the boil. Cover and simmer for 40 minutes, or until tender and the liquid is absorbed.

3   Heat the remaining oil in a large frying pan and add the mushrooms. Cook for 5 minutes until golden. Stir in the duck and garlic and cook for 2–3 minutes to heat through. Season well.

4   To make the dressing, whisk the vinegars, mustard and honey in a large serving bowl, then gradually whisk in the oils. Add the lentils and the rice, then stir lightly together. Gently stir in the ham, blanched courgettes, spring onions and parsley. Season to taste and sprinkle with the walnuts. Serve topped with the duck and mushrooms.

Brown Rice Spiced Pilaf

Nutritional details

per 100 g

energy	90 kcals/376 kj
protein	2 g
carbohydrate	15 g
fat	2.5 g
fibre	1.1 g
sugar	5 g
sodium	0.3 g

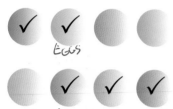

Eggs

V

Ingredients   Serves 4

1 tbsp vegetable oil
1 tbsp blanched almonds,
    flaked or chopped
1 onion, peeled and chopped
1 carrot, peeled and diced
225 g/8 oz flat mushrooms,
    sliced thickly
¼ tsp cinnamon
large pinch dried chilli flakes
50 g/2 oz dried apricots,
    roughly chopped
25 g/1 oz currants
zest of 1 orange
350 g/12 oz brown basmati rice
900 ml/1½ pints vegetable stock
2 tbsp freshly chopped coriander
2 tbsp freshly snipped chives
salt and freshly ground black pepper
snipped chives, to garnish

Step-by-step guide

1 Preheat the oven to 200°C/
   400°F/Gas Mark 6. Heat the oil
   in a large flameproof casserole
   dish and add the almonds.
   Cook for 1–2 minutes until just
   browning. Be very careful as the
   nuts will burn easily.

2 Add the onion and carrot. Cook
   for 5 minutes until softened and
   starting to turn brown. Add the
   mushrooms and cook for a further
   5 minutes, stirring often.

3 Add the cinnamon and chilli flakes
   and cook for about 30 seconds
   before adding the apricots,
   currants, orange zest and rice.

4 Stir together well and add the
   stock. Bring to the boil, cover
   tightly and transfer to the
   preheated oven. Cook for
   45 minutes until the rice
   and vegetables are tender.

5 Stir the coriander and chives
   into the pilaf and season to
   taste with salt and pepper.
   Garnish with the extra chives
   and serve immediately.

cows' milk-free   egg-free   gluten-free   wheat-free   nut-free   vegetarian   vegan   seafood-free

Cheese & Onion Oat Pie

Nutritional details

per 100 g

energy	187 kcals/781 kj
protein	8 g
carbohydrate	18 g
fat	10 g
fibre	1 g
sugar	2 g
sodium	0.2 g

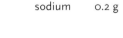

EGGS

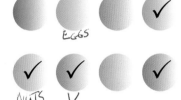

NUTS   V

Ingredients   Serves 4

1 tbsp sunflower oil, plus 1 tsp
25 g/1 oz butter
2 medium onions, peeled and sliced
1 garlic clove, peeled and crushed
150 g/5 oz porridge oats
125 g/4 oz mature Cheddar
    cheese, grated
2 medium eggs, lightly beaten
2 tbsp freshly chopped parsley
salt and freshly ground black pepper
275 g/10 oz baking potato, peeled

Step-by-step guide

1 Preheat the oven to 180°C/350°F/ Gas Mark 4. Heat the oil and half the butter in a saucepan until melted. Add the onions and garlic and gently cook for 10 minutes, or until soft. Remove from the heat and tip into a large bowl.

2 Spread the oats out on a baking sheet and toast in the hot oven for 12 minutes. Leave to cool, then add to the onions with the cheese, eggs and parsley. Season to taste with salt and pepper and mix well.

3 Line the base of a 20.5 cm/ 8 inch round sandwich tin with greaseproof paper and oil well. Thinly slice the potato and arrange the slices on the base, overlapping them slightly.

4 Spoon the cheese and oat mixture on top of the potato, spreading

evenly with the back of a spoon. Cover with tinfoil and bake for 30 minutes.

5 Invert the pie onto a baking sheet so that the potatoes are on top. Carefully remove the tin and lining paper.

6 Preheat the grill to medium. Melt the remaining butter and carefully brush over the potato topping. Cook under the preheated grill for 5–6 minutes until the potatoes are lightly browned. Cut into wedges and serve.

cows' milk-free   egg-free   gluten-free   wheat-free   nut-free   vegetarian   vegan   seafood-free

Chicken & Baby Vegetable Stir Fry

Nutritional details

per 100 g

energy	69 kcals/286 kj
protein	6 g
carbohydrate	2 g
fat	4 g
fibre	1.5 g
sugar	1.8 g
sodium	0.3 g

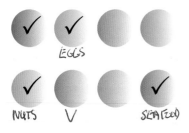

EGGS

NUTS V SEAFOOD

Ingredients   Serves 4

2 tbsp sunflower oil
1 small red chilli,
  deseeded and finely chopped
150 g/5 oz chicken breast
  or thigh meat,
  skinned and cut into cubes
2 baby leeks, trimmed and sliced
12 asparagus spears, halved
125 g/4 oz mangetout, trimmed
125 g/4 oz baby carrots, trimmed
  and halved lengthways
125 g/4 oz fine green beans,
  trimmed and diagonally sliced
125 g/4 oz baby sweetcorn,
  diagonally halved
50 ml/2 fl oz chicken stock
2 tsp light soy sauce
1 tbsp dry sherry
1 tsp sesame oil
toasted sesame seeds,
  to garnish

Step-by-step guide

1 Heat the wok until very hot and add the oil. Add the chopped chilli and chicken and stir-fry for 4–5 minutes, or until the chicken is cooked and golden.

2 Increase the heat, add the leeks to the chicken and stir-fry for 2 minutes. Add the asparagus spears, mangetout, baby carrots, green beans, and baby sweetcorn. Stir-fry for 3–4 minutes, or until the vegetables soften slightly but still retain a slight crispness.

3 In a small bowl, mix together the chicken stock, soy sauce, dry sherry and sesame oil. Pour into the wok, stir and cook until heated through. Sprinkle with the toasted sesame seeds and serve immediately.

cows' milk-free egg-free gluten-free wheat-free nut-free vegetarian vegan seafood-free

Chilli Con Carne with Crispy-skinned Potatoes

Nutritional details

per 100 g

energy	117 kcals/493 kj
protein	7 g
carbohydrate	15 g
fat	3.5 g
fibre	2.1 g
sugar	2.2 g
sodium	0.1 g

Ingredients   Serves 4

2 tbsp vegetable oil,
    plus extra for brushing
1 large onion,
    peeled and finely chopped
1 garlic clove,
    peeled and finely chopped
1 red chilli, deseeded and
    finely chopped
450 g/1 lb chuck steak, finely
    chopped, or lean beef mince
1 tbsp chilli powder
400 g can chopped tomatoes
2 tbsp tomato purée
400 g can red kidney beans,
    drained and rinsed
4 large baking potatoes
coarse salt and freshly
    ground black pepper

To serve:
ready-made guacamole
soured cream

Step-by-step guide

1   Preheat the oven to 150°C/300°F/ Gas Mark 2. Heat the oil in a large flameproof casserole dish and add the onion. Cook gently for 10 minutes until soft and lightly browned. Add the garlic and chilli and cook briefly. Increase the heat. Add the chuck steak or lean mince and cook for a further 10 minutes, stirring occasionally, until browned.

2   Add the chilli powder and stir well. Cook for about 2 minutes, then add the chopped tomatoes and tomato purée. Bring slowly to the boil. Cover and cook in the preheated oven for 1½ hours. Remove from the oven and stir in the kidney beans. Return to the oven for a further 15 minutes.

3   Meanwhile, brush a little vegetable oil all over the potatoes and rub on some coarse salt. Put the potatoes in the oven alongside the chilli.

4   Remove the chilli and potatoes from the oven. Cut a cross in each potato, then squeeze to open slightly and season to taste with salt and pepper. Serve with the chilli, guacamole and soured cream.

Chinese Steamed Sea Bass with Black Beans

Nutritional details

per 100 g

energy	147 kcals/614 kj
protein	21 g
carbohydrate	1 g
fat	5 g
fibre	1 g
sugar	0.3 g
sodium	0.4 g

Ingredients   Serves 4

1.1 kg/2½ lb sea bass, cleaned with
   head and tail left on
1–2 tbsp rice wine or dry sherry
1½ tbsp sunflower oil
2–3 tbsp fermented black beans,
   rinsed and drained
1 garlic clove, peeled and
   finely chopped
1 cm/½ inch piece fresh root ginger,
   peeled and finely chopped
4 spring onions, trimmed and thinly
   sliced diagonally
2–3 tbsp soy sauce
125 ml/4 fl oz fish or chicken stock
1–2 tbsp sweet Chinese chilli sauce,
   or to taste
2 tsp sesame oil
sprigs of fresh coriander,
   to garnish

Step-by-step guide

1 Using a sharp knife, cut 3–4 deep diagonal slashes along both sides of the fish. Sprinkle the Chinese rice wine or sherry inside and over the fish and gently rub into the skin on both sides.

2 Lightly brush a heatproof plate large enough to fit into a large wok or frying pan with a little of the sunflower oil. Place the fish on the plate, curving the fish along the inside edge of the dish, then leave for 20 minutes.

3 Place a wire rack or inverted ramekin in the wok and pour in enough water to come about 2.5 cm/1 inch up the side. Bring to the boil over a high heat.

4 Carefully place the plate with the fish on the rack or ramekin, cover and steam for 12–15 minutes, or until the fish is tender and the flesh is opaque when pierced with a knife near the bone.

5 Remove the plate with the fish from the wok and keep warm. Remove the rack or ramekin from the wok and pour off the water. Return the wok to the heat, add the remaining sunflower oil and swirl to coat the bottom and side. Add the black beans, garlic and ginger and stir-fry for 1 minute.

6 Add the spring onions, soy sauce, fish or chicken stock and boil for 1 minute. Stir in the chilli sauce and sesame oil, then pour the sauce over the cooked fish. Garnish with coriander sprigs and serve immediately.

✔ cows' milk-free ✔ egg-free ✔ gluten-free ✔ wheat-free ✔ nut-free ✔ vegetarian ✔ vegan ✔ seafood-free

Cream of Pumpkin Soup

Nutritional details

per 100 g

energy	62 kcals/260 kj
protein	2 g
carbohydrate	8 g
fat	3 g
fibre	1.3 g
sugar	2.5 g
sodium	0.1 g

Ingredients   Serves 4

900 g/2 lb pumpkin flesh
   (after peeling and discarding
   the seeds)
4 tbsp olive oil
1 large onion, peeled
1 leek, trimmed
1 carrot, peeled
2 celery sticks
4 garlic cloves, peeled and crushed
1.7 litres/3 pints water
salt and freshly ground black pepper
¼ tsp freshly grated nutmeg
150 ml/¼ pint single cream
¼ tsp cayenne pepper

Step-by-step guide

1 Cut the skinned and de-seeded pumpkin flesh into 2.5 cm/1 inch cubes. Heat the olive oil in a large saucepan and cook the pumpkin for 2–3 minutes, coating it completely with oil. Chop the onion and leek finely and cut the carrot and celery into small cubes.

2 Add the vegetables to the saucepan with the garlic and cook, stirring for 5 minutes, or until they have begun to soften. Cover the vegetables with the water and bring to the boil. Season with plenty of salt and pepper and the nutmeg, then cover and simmer for 15–20 minutes, or until all of the vegetables are tender.

3 When the vegetables are tender, remove from the heat, cool slightly then pour into a food processor or blender. Liquidise to form a smooth purée then pass through a sieve into a clean saucepan.

4 Adjust the seasoning to taste and add all but 2 tablespoons of the cream and enough water to obtain the correct consistency. Bring the soup to boiling point, add the cayenne pepper and serve immediately swirled with cream.

Creamy Puy Lentils

Nutritional details

per 100 g

energy	84 kcals/353 kj
protein	4 g
carbohydrate	10 g
fat	4 g
fibre	2.2 g
sugar	1 g
sodium	0.3 g

Ingredients   Serves 4

225 g/8 oz puy lentils
1 tbsp olive oil
1 garlic clove,
    peeled and finely chopped
zest and juice of 1 lemon
1 tsp wholegrain mustard
1 tbsp freshly chopped tarragon
3 tbsp half-fat crème fraîche
salt and freshly ground black pepper
2 small tomatoes,
    deseeded and chopped
50 g/2 oz pitted black olives
1 tbsp freshly chopped parsley

To garnish:
sprigs of fresh tarragon

Step-by-step guide

1   Put the lentils in a saucepan with plenty of cold water and bring to the boil.

2   Boil rapidly for 10 minutes, reduce the heat and simmer gently for a further 20 minutes until just tender. Drain well.

3   Meanwhile, prepare the dressing. Heat the oil in a frying pan over a medium heat.

4   Add the garlic and cook for about a minute until just beginning to brown. Add the lemon zest and juice.

5   Add the mustard and cook for a further 30 seconds.

6   Add the tarragon and crème fraîche and season to taste with salt and pepper.

7   Simmer and add the drained lentils, tomatoes and olives.

8   Transfer to a serving dish and sprinkle the chopped parsley on top.

9   Garnish the lentils with the tarragon sprigs and the lemon wedges and serve immediately.

✓ cows' milk-free   ✓ egg-free   ✓ gluten-free   ✓ wheat-free   ✓ nut-free   ✓ vegetarian   ✓ vegan   ✓ seafood-free

Crispy Baked Potatoes with Serrano Ham

Nutritional details

per 100 g

energy	126 kcals/536 kj
protein	5 g
carbohydrate	24 g
fat	2 g
fibre	2.6 g
sugar	1.4 g
sodium	0.1 g

Ingredients   Serves 4

4 large baking potatoes
4 tsp half-fat crème fraîche
salt and freshly ground
    black pepper
50 g/2 oz lean serrano ham or
    prosciutto, with fat removed
50 g/2 oz cooked baby
    broad beans
50 g/2 oz cooked carrots, diced
50 g/2 oz cooked peas
50 g/2 oz low-fat hard
    cheese such as Edam
    or Cheddar, grated
fresh green salad, to serve

Step-by-step guide

1 Preheat the oven to 200°C/
400°F/Gas Mark 6. Scrub
the potatoes dry. Prick with a fork
and place on a baking sheet. Cook
for 1–1½ hours or until tender
when squeezed. Use oven gloves
or a kitchen towel to pick up the
potatoes as they will be very hot.

2 Cut the potatoes in half
horizontally and scoop out
all the flesh into a bowl.

3 Spoon the crème fraîche into the
bowl and mix thoroughly with the
potatoes. Season to taste with a
little salt and pepper.

4 Cut the ham into strips and
carefully stir into the potato
mixture with the broad beans,
carrots and peas.

5 Pile the mixture back into the
eight potato shells and sprinkle a
little grated cheese on the top.

6 Place under a hot grill and cook
until golden and heated through.
Serve immediately with a fresh
green salad.

cows' milk-free   egg-free   gluten-free   wheat-free   nut-free   vegetarian   vegan   seafood-free

Mixed Grain Bread

Nutritional details

per 100 g

energy	338 kcals/1425 kj
protein	13 g
carbohydrate	64 g
fat	5 g
fibre	1.3 g
sugar	0.7 g
sodium	0.6 g

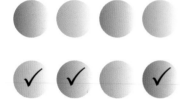

Makes 1 large loaf

350 g/12 oz strong white flour
2 tsp salt
225 g/8 oz strong Granary flour
125 g/4 oz rye flour
25 g/1 oz butter, diced
2 tsp easy-blend dried yeast
25 g/1 oz rolled oats
2 tbsp sunflower seeds
1 tbsp malt extract
450 ml/¾ pint warm water
1 medium egg, beaten

Step-by-step guide

1 Preheat the oven to 220°C/425°F/ Gas Mark 7, 15 minutes before baking. Sift the white flour and salt into a large bowl. Stir in the Granary and rye flours, then rub in the butter until the mixture resembles breadcrumbs. Stir in the yeast, oats and seeds and make a well in the centre.

2 Stir the malt extract into the warm water until dissolved. Add the malt water to the dry ingredients. Mix to a soft dough.

3 Turn the dough out on to a lightly floured surface and knead for 10 minutes, until smooth and elastic.

4 Put in an oiled bowl, cover with clingfilm and leave to rise in a warm place for 1½ hours or until doubled in size.

5 Turn out and knead again for a minute or two to knock out the air.

6 Shape into an oval loaf about 30.5 cm/12 inches long and place on a well-oiled baking sheet.

7 Cover with oiled clingfilm and leave to rise for 40 minutes, or until doubled in size

8 Brush the loaf with beaten egg and bake in the preheated oven for 35–45 minutes, or until the bread is well risen, browned and sounds hollow when the base is tapped. Leave to cool on a wire rack, then serve.

✓ cows' milk-free   ✓ egg-free   ✓ gluten-free   ✓ wheat-free   ✓ nut-free   ✓ vegetarian   ✓ vegan   ✓ seafood-free

Mixed Grain Pilaf

Nutritional details

per 100 g

energy	98 kcals/412 kj
protein	5 g
carbohydrate	10 g
fat	4 g
fibre	2.5 g
sugar	2.3 g
sodium	0.3 g

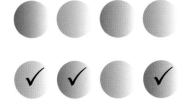

Ingredients   Serves 4

2 tbsp olive oil
1 garlic clove,
    peeled and crushed
½ tsp ground turmeric
125 g/4 oz mixed long-grain
    and wild rice
50 g/2 oz red lentils
300 ml/½ pint vegetable stock
200 g can chopped tomatoes
5 cm/2 inch piece cinnamon stick
salt and freshly ground
    black pepper
400 g can mixed beans,
    drained and rinsed
15 g/½ oz butter
1 bunch spring onions,
    trimmed and finely sliced
3 medium eggs
4 tbsp freshly chopped herbs,
    such as parsley and chervil
sprigs of fresh dill, to garnish

Step-by-step guide

1   Heat 1 tablespoon of the oil in a saucepan. Add the garlic and turmeric and cook for a few seconds. Stir in the rice and lentils.

2   Add the stock, tomatoes and cinnamon. Season to taste with salt and pepper. Stir once and bring to the boil. Lower the heat, cover and simmer for 20 minutes, until most of the stock is absorbed and the rice and lentils are tender.

3   Stir in the beans, replace the lid and leave to stand for 2–3 minutes to allow the beans to heat through.

4   While the rice is cooking, heat the remaining oil and butter in a frying pan. Add the spring onions and cook for 4–5 minutes, until soft. Lightly beat the eggs with 2 tablespoons of the herbs, then season with salt and pepper.

5   Pour the egg mixture over the spring onions. Stir gently with a spatula over a low heat, drawing the mixture from the sides to the centre as the omelette sets. When almost set, stop stirring and cook for about 30 seconds until golden underneath.

6   Remove the omelette from the pan, roll up and slice into thin strips. Fluff the rice up with a fork and remove the cinnamon stick. Spoon onto serving plates, top with strips of omelette and the remaining chopped herbs. Garnish with sprigs of dill and serve.

Oven-roasted Vegetables with Sausages

Nutritional details

per 100 g

energy	82 kcals/341 kj
protein	4 g
carbohydrate	9 g
fat	3 g
fibre	0.8 g
sugar	0.3 g
sodium	0.1 g

Ingredients   Serves 4

2 medium aubergines, trimmed
3 medium courgettes, trimmed
4 tbsp olive oil
6 garlic cloves
8 Tuscany-style sausages
4 plum tomatoes
2 x 300 g cans cannellini beans
salt and freshly ground black pepper
1 bunch of fresh basil, torn into
    coarse pieces
4 tbsp Parmesan cheese, grated

Step-by-step guide

1 Preheat the oven to 200°C/400°F/ Gas Mark 6, 15 minutes before cooking. Cut the aubergines and courgettes into bite-sized chunks. Place the olive oil in a large roasting tin and heat in the preheated oven for 3 minutes, or until very hot. Add the aubergines, courgettes and garlic cloves, then stir until coated in the hot oil and cook in the oven for 10 minutes.

2 Remove the roasting tin from the oven and stir. Lightly prick the sausages, add to the roasting tin and return to the oven. Continue to roast for a further 20 minutes, turning once during cooking, until the vegetables are tender and the sausages are golden brown.

3 Meanwhile, roughly chop the plum tomatoes and drain the cannellini beans. Remove the sausages from the oven and stir in the tomatoes and cannellini beans. Season to taste with salt and pepper, then return to the oven for 5 minutes, or until heated thoroughly.

4 Scatter over the basil leaves and sprinkle with plenty of Parmesan cheese and extra freshly ground black pepper. Serve immediately.

cows' milk-free   egg-free   gluten-free   wheat-free   nut-free   vegetarian   vegan   seafood-free

Pasta & Pork Ragù

Nutritional details

per 100 g

energy	117 kcals/489 kj
protein	9 g
carbohydrate	13 g
fat	3 g
fibre	1 g
sugar	1 g
sodium	0.1 g

Ingredients   Serves 4

1 tbsp sunflower oil
1 leek, trimmed and thinly sliced
225 g/8 oz pork fillet, diced
1 garlic clove, peeled and crushed
2 tsp paprika
¼ tsp cayenne pepper
150 ml/¼ pint white wine
600 ml/1 pint vegetable stock
400g can borlotti beans,
    drained and rinsed
2 carrots, peeled and diced
salt and freshly ground
    black pepper
225 g/8 oz fresh egg tagliatelle
1 tbsp freshly chopped parsley,
    to garnish
crème fraîche, to serve

Step-by-step guide

1   Heat the sunflower oil in a large frying pan. Add the sliced leek and cook, stirring frequently, for 5 minutes, or until softened. Add the pork and cook, stirring, for 4 minutes, or until sealed.

2   Add the crushed garlic and the paprika and cayenne peppers to the pan and stir until all the pork is lightly coated in the garlic and pepper mixture.

3   Pour in the wine and 450 ml/¾ pint of the vegetable stock. Add the borlotti beans and carrots and season to taste with salt and pepper. Bring the sauce to the boil, then lower the heat and simmer for 5 minutes.

4   Meanwhile, place the egg tagliatelle in a large saucepan of lightly salted, boiling water, then cover and simmer for 5 minutes, or until the pasta is 'al dente'.

5   Drain the pasta, then add to the pork ragù and toss well. Adjust the seasoning, then tip into a warmed serving dish. Sprinkle with chopped parsley and serve with a little crème fraîche.

Pork in Peanut Sauce

Nutritional details

per 100 g

energy	117 kcals/490 kj
protein	11 g
carbohydrate	8 g
fat	5 g
fibre	1 g
sugar	1.9 g
sodium	0.2 g

Ingredients   Serves 4

450 g/1 lb pork fillet
2 tbsp light soy sauce
1 tbsp vinegar
1 tsp sugar
1 tsp Chinese five spice powder
2–4 garlic cloves, peeled and crushed
2 tbsp groundnut oil
1 large onion, peeled and finely sliced
125 g/4 oz carrots, peeled and
   cut into matchsticks
2 celery sticks, trimmed and sliced
125 g/4 oz French beans,
   trimmed and halved
3 tbsp smooth peanut butter
1 tbsp freshly chopped flat leaf parsley

To serve:
freshly cooked basmati and wild rice
green salad

Step-by-step guide

1 Remove any fat or sinew from the pork fillet, cut into thin strips and reserve. Blend the soy sauce, vinegar, sugar, Chinese five spice powder and garlic in a bowl and add the pork. Cover and leave to marinate in the refrigerator for at least 30 minutes.

2 Drain the pork, reserving any marinade. Heat the wok, then add the oil and, when hot, stir-fry the pork for 3–4 minutes, or until sealed.

3 Add the onion, carrots, celery and beans to the wok and stir-fry for 4–5 minutes, or until the meat is tender and the vegetables are softened.

4 Blend the reserved marinade, the peanut butter and 2 tablespoons of hot water together. When smooth, stir into the wok and cook for several minutes more until the sauce is thick and the pork is piping hot. Sprinkle with the chopped parsley and serve immediately with the basmati and wild rice and a green salad.

✓ cows' milk-free   ✓ egg-free   ✓ gluten-free   ✓ wheat-free   ✓ nut-free   ✓ vegetarian   ✓ vegan   ✓ seafood-free

Pork with Black Bean Sauce

Nutritional details

per 100 g

energy	131 kcals/548 kj
protein	14 g
carbohydrate	9 g
fat	4 g
fibre	0.7 g
sugar	1.2 g
sodium	0.4 g

Ingredients   Serves 4

700 g/1½ lb pork tenderloin
4 tbsp light soy sauce
2 tbsp groundnut oil
1 garlic clove, peeled and chopped
2.5 cm/1 inch piece fresh root ginger,
    peeled and cut into matchsticks
1 large carrot, peeled and sliced
1 red pepper, deseeded and sliced
1 green pepper, deseeded and sliced
160 g jar black bean sauce
salt
snipped fresh chives, to garnish
freshly steamed rice, to serve

Step-by-step guide

1   Using a sharp knife, trim the pork, discarding any fat or sinew and cut into bite-sized chunks. Place in a large shallow dish and spoon over the soy sauce. Turn to coat evenly, cover with clingfilm and leave to marinate for at least 30 minutes in the refrigerator. When ready to use, lift the pork from the marinade, shaking off as much marinade as possible, and pat dry with absorbent kitchen paper. Reserve the marinade.

2   Heat a wok, add the groundnut oil and when hot, add the chopped garlic and ginger and stir-fry for 30 seconds. Add the carrot and the red and green peppers and stir-fry for 3–4 minutes or until just softened.

3   Add the pork to the wok and stir-fry for 5–7 minutes, or until browned all over and tender. Pour in the reserved marinade and black bean sauce. Bring to the boil, stirring constantly until well blended, then simmer for 1 minute until heated through thoroughly. Tip into a warmed serving dish or spoon on to individual plates. Garnish with snipped chives and serve immediately with steamed rice.

✓ cows' milk-free ✓ egg-free ✓ gluten-free ✓ wheat-free ✓ nut-free ✓ vegetarian ✓ vegan ✓ seafood-free

Potato Skins

Nutritional details

per 100 g

energy	222 kcals/927 kj
protein	6 g
carbohydrate	20 g
fat	8 g
fibre	1.7 g
sugar	1.2 g
sodium	0.3 g

Ingredients   Serves 4

4 large baking potatoes
2 tbsp olive oil
2 tsp paprika
125 g/4 oz pancetta,
    roughly chopped
6 tbsp double cream
125 g/4 oz Gorgonzola cheese
1 tbsp freshly chopped parsley

To serve:
mayonnaise
sweet chilli dipping sauce

Step-by-step guide

1 Preheat the oven to 200°C/400°F/
Gas Mark 6. Scrub the potatoes,
then prick a few times with a fork
or skewer and place directly on
the top shelf of the oven. Bake in
the preheated oven for at least 1
hour, or until tender. The potatoes
are cooked when they yield gently
to the pressure of your hand.

2 Set the potatoes aside until cool
enough to handle, then cut in half
and scoop the flesh into a bowl
and reserve. Preheat the grill and
line the grill rack with tinfoil.

3 Mix together the oil and the
paprika and use half to brush the
outside of the potato skins. Place
on the grill rack under the
preheated hot grill and cook for
5 minutes, or until crisp, turning
as necessary.

4 Heat the remaining paprika-
flavoured oil and gently fry the
pancetta until crisp. Add to the
potato flesh along with the cream,
Gorgonzola cheese and parsley.
Halve the potato skins and fill with
the Gorgonzola filling. Return to the
oven for a further 15 minutes to heat
through. Sprinkle with a little more
paprika and serve immediately with
mayonnaise, sweet chilli sauce and
a green salad.

✓ cows' milk-free ✓ egg-free ✓ gluten-free ✓ wheat-free ✓ nut-free ✓ vegetarian ✓ vegan ✓ seafood-free

Red Lentil Kedgeree with Avocado & Tomatoes

Nutritional details

per 100 g

energy	138 kcals/575 kj
protein	3 g
carbohydrate	13 g
fat	5 g
fibre	1.5 g
sugar	1.6 g
sodium	0.3 g

Ingredients   Serves 4

150 g/5 oz basmati rice
150 g/5 oz red lentils
15 g/½ oz butter
1 tbsp sunflower oil
1 medium onion,
     peeled and chopped
1 tsp ground cumin
4 cardamom pods, bruised
1 bay leaf
450 ml/¾ pint vegetable stock
1 ripe avocado, peeled,
     stoned and diced
1 tbsp lemon juice
4 plum tomatoes,
     peeled and diced
2 tbsp freshly chopped coriander
salt and freshly ground
     black pepper
lemon or lime slices,
     to garnish

Step-by-step guide

1 Put the rice and lentils in a sieve and rinse under cold running water. Tip into a bowl, then pour over enough cold water to cover and leave to soak for 10 minutes.

2 Heat the butter and oil in a saucepan. Add the sliced onion and cook gently, stirring occasionally, for 10 minutes until softened. Stir in the cumin, cardamon pods and bay leaf and cook for a further minute, stirring all the time.

3 Drain the rice and lentils, rinse again and add to the onions in the saucepan. Stir in the vegetable stock and bring to the boil. Reduce the heat, cover the saucepan and simmer for about 15 minutes, or until the rice and lentils are tender.

4 Place the diced avocado in a bowl and toss with the lemon juice. Stir in the tomatoes and chopped coriander. Season to taste with salt and pepper.

5 Fluff up the rice with a fork, spoon into a warmed serving dish and spoon the avocado mixture on top. Garnish with lemon or lime slices and serve.

cows' milk-free   egg-free   gluten-free   wheat-free   nut-free   vegetarian   vegan   seafood-free

Roast Butternut Squash Risotto

Nutritional details

per 100 g

energy	88 kcals/368 kj
protein	3 g
carbohydrate	11 g
fat	4 g
fibre	0.8 g
sugar	0.1 g
sodium	0.2 g

Ingredients   Serves 4

1 medium butternut squash
2 tbsp olive oil
1 garlic bulb, cloves separated,
    but unpeeled
15 g/½ oz unsalted butter
275 g/10 oz Arborio rice
large pinch of saffron strands
150 ml/¼ pint dry white wine
1 litre/1¾ pints vegetable stock
1 tbsp freshly chopped parsley
1 tbsp freshly chopped oregano
50 g/2 oz Parmesan cheese,
    finely grated
salt and freshly ground black pepper
sprigs of fresh oregano, to garnish
extra Parmesan cheese, to serve

Step-by-step guide

1   Preheat the oven to 190°C/
    375°F/Gas Mark 5. Cut the squash
    in half, peel, then scoop out the
    seeds and discard. Cut the flesh
    into 2 cm/¾ inch cubes.

2   Pour the oil into a large roasting
    tin and heat in the preheated oven
    for 5 minutes. Add the butternut
    squash and garlic cloves. Turn in
    the oil to coat, then roast in the
    oven for about 25–30 minutes, or
    until golden brown and very
    tender, turning the vegetables
    halfway through cooking time.

3   Melt the butter in a large
    saucepan. Add the rice and stir
    over a high heat for a few
    seconds. Add the saffron and the
    wine and bubble fiercely until
    almost totally reduced, stirring
    frequently. At the same time heat

the stock in a separate saucepan
and keep at a steady simmer.

4   Reduce the heat under the rice to
    low. Add a ladleful of stock to the
    saucepan and simmer, stirring,
    until absorbed. Continue adding
    the stock in this way until the rice
    is tender. This will take about
    20 minutes and it may not be
    necessary to add all the stock.

5   Turn off the heat, stir in the herbs,
    Parmesan cheese and seasoning.
    Cover and leave to stand for 2–3
    minutes. Quickly remove the skins
    from the roasted garlic. Add to the
    risotto with the butternut squash
    and mix gently. Garnish with sprigs
    of oregano and serve immediately
    with Parmesan cheese.

✔ cows' milk-free ✔ egg-free ✔ gluten-free ✔ wheat-free ✔ nut-free ✔ vegetarian ✔ vegan ✔ seafood-free

Roasted Butternut Squash

Nutritional details

per 100 g

energy	54 kcals/224 kj
protein	2 g
carbohydrate	9 g
fat	1 g
fibre	1 g
sugar	0.9 g
sodium	trace

Ingredients   Serves 4

2 small butternut squash
4 garlic cloves, peeled
    and crushed
1 tbsp olive oil
salt and freshly ground
    black pepper
1 tbsp olive oil
4 medium-sized leeks, trimmed,
    cleaned and thinly sliced
1 tbsp black mustard seeds
300 g can cannellini beans,
    drained and rinsed
125 g/4 oz fine French
    beans, halved
150 ml/¼ pint vegetable stock
50 g/2 oz rocket
2 tbsp freshly snipped chives
fresh chives, to garnish

To serve:
4 tbsp fromage frais
mixed salad

Step-by-step guide

1 Preheat the oven to 200°C/400°F/
   Gas Mark 6. Cut the butternut
   squash in half lengthwise and
   scoop out all of the seeds.

2 Score the squash in a diamond
   pattern with a sharp knife. Mix the
   garlic with the olive oil and brush
   over the cut surfaces of the
   squash. Season well with salt and
   pepper. Put on a baking sheet and
   roast for 40 minutes until tender.

3 Heat the olive oil in a saucepan
   and fry the leeks and mustard
   seeds for 5 minutes.

4 Add the drained cannellini beans,
   French beans and vegetable stock.
   Bring to the boil and simmer
   gently for 5 minutes until the
   French beans are tender.

5 Remove from the heat and
   stir in the rocket and chives.
   Season well. Remove the squash
   from the oven and allow to cool
   for 5 minutes. Spoon in the bean
   mixture. Garnish with a few
   snipped chives and serve
   immediately with the fromage
   frais and a mixed salad.

✓ cows' milk-free   ✓ egg-free   ✓ gluten-free   ✓ wheat-free   ✓ nut-free   ✓ vegetarian   ✓ vegan   ✓ seafood-free

Roasted Vegetable Pie

Nutritional details

per 100 g

energy	139 kcals/579 kj
protein	4 g
carbohydrate	13 g
fat	8 g
fibre	1.1 g
sugar	1.9 g
sodium	0.1 g

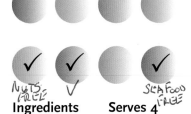

NUTS FREE ✓   V ✓   SEAFOOD FREE ✓

Ingredients   Serves 4

225 g/8 oz plain flour
pinch of salt
50 g/2 oz white vegetable fat,
    cut into squares
50 g/2 oz butter, cut into squares
2 tsp herbes de Provence
1 red pepper, deseeded and halved
1 green pepper, deseeded and halved
1 yellow pepper, deseeded and halved
3 tbsp extra virgin olive oil
1 aubergine, trimmed and sliced
1 courgette, trimmed and
    halved lengthways
1 leek, trimmed and cut into chunks
1 medium egg, beaten
125 g/4 oz fresh mozzarella
    cheese, sliced
salt and freshly ground black pepper
sprigs of mixed herbs, to garnish

Step-by-step guide

1 Preheat the oven to 220°C/425°F/
  Gas Mark 7. Sift the flour and salt
  into a large bowl, add the fats and
  mix lightly. Using the fingertips rub
  into the flour until the mixture
  resembles breadcrumbs. Stir in the
  herbes de Provence. Sprinkle over
  a tablespoon of cold water and with
  a knife start bringing the dough
  together – it may be necessary to
  use your hands for the final stage.
  If the dough does not form a ball
  instantly, add a little more water.
  Place the pastry in a polythene bag
  and chill for 30 minutes.

2 Place the peppers on a baking tray
  and sprinkle with 1 tablespoon of
  oil. Roast in the preheated oven
  for 20 minutes or until the skins
  start to blacken. Brush the
  aubergines, courgettes and leeks
  with oil and place on another
  baking tray. Roast in the oven with
  the peppers for 20 minutes.

3 Place the blackened peppers in a
  polythene bag and leave the skin
  to loosen for 5 minutes. When
  cool enough to handle, peel the
  skins off the peppers.

4 Roll out half the pastry on a lightly
  floured surface and use to line a
  20.5 cm/8 inch round pie dish.
  Line the pastry with greaseproof
  paper and fill with baking beans or
  rice and bake blind for about 10
  minutes. Remove the beans and
  the paper, then brush the base
  with a little of the beaten egg.
  Return to the oven for 5 minutes.

5 Layer the cooked vegetables and
  the cheese in the pastry case,
  seasoning each layer. Roll out the
  remaining pastry on a lightly
  floured surface, and cut out the
  lid 5 mm/¼ inch wider than the
  dish. Brush the rim with the
  beaten egg and lay the pastry lid
  on top, pressing to seal. Knock
  the edges with the back of a knife.
  Cut a slit in the lid and brush with
  the beaten egg. Bake for 30
  minutes. Transfer to a large
  serving dish, garnish with sprigs
  of mixed herbs and serve.

✓ cows' milk-free   ✓ egg-free   ✓ gluten-free   ✓ wheat-free   ✓ nut-free   ✓ vegetarian   ✓ vegan   ✓ seafood-free

Smoked Salmon with Broad Beans & Rice

Nutritional details

per 100 g

energy	133 kcals/554 kj
protein	8 g
carbohydrate	10 g
fat	5 g
fibre	1 g
sugar	0.9 g
sodium	0.4 g

EGGS FREE

NUT FREE

Ingredients   Serves 4

2 tbsp sunflower oil
25 g/1 oz unsalted butter
1 onion, peeled and chopped
2 garlic cloves,
   peeled and chopped
175 g/6 oz asparagus tips, halved
75 g/3 oz frozen broad beans
150 ml/¼ pint dry white wine
125 g/4 oz sun-dried tomatoes,
   drained and sliced
125 g/4 oz baby spinach
   leaves, washed
450 g/1 lb cooked long-grain rice
3 tbsp crème fraîche
225 g/8 oz smoked salmon,
   cut into strips
75 g/3 oz freshly grated
   Parmesan cheese
salt and freshly ground
   black pepper

Step-by-step guide

1 Heat a large wok, then add the oil and butter and, when melted, stir-fry the onion for 3 minutes until almost softened. Add the garlic and asparagus tips and stir-fry for 3 minutes. Add the broad beans and wine and bring to the boil, then simmer, stirring occasionally, until the wine is reduced slightly.

2 Add the sun-dried tomatoes and bring back to the boil, then simmer for 2 minutes. Stir in the baby spinach leaves and cooked rice and return to the boil. Stir-fry for 2 minutes, or until the spinach is wilted and the rice is heated through thoroughly.

3 Stir in the crème fraîche, smoked salmon strips and Parmesan cheese. Stir well and cook, stirring frequently, until piping hot. Season to taste with salt and pepper. Serve immediately.

Spicy Chilli Beef

Nutritional details

per 100 g

energy	123 kcals/518 kj
protein	8 g
carbohydrate	12 g
fat	5 g
fibre	1.9 g
sugar	3.8 g
sodium	0.1 g

NUTS FREE

Ingredients   Serves 4

2 tbsp olive oil
1 onion, peeled and finely chopped
1 red pepper, deseeded and sliced
450 g/1 lb minced beef steak
2 garlic cloves, peeled and crushed
2 red chillies, deseeded and
    finely sliced
salt and freshly ground black pepper
400 g can chopped tomatoes
2 tbsp tomato purée
400 g can red kidney beans, drained
50 g/2 oz good quality, plain dark
    chocolate, grated
350 g/12 oz dried fusilli pasta
2 tbsp freshly chopped
    flat leaf parsley
paprika, to garnish
soured cream, to serve

Step-by-step guide

1   Heat the olive oil in a large, heavy-based pan. Add the onion and red pepper and cook for 5 minutes, or until beginning to soften. Add the minced beef and cook over a high heat for 5–8 minutes, or until the meat is browned. Stir with a wooden spoon during cooking to break up any lumps in the meat. Add the garlic and chilli, fry for 1 minute then season to taste with salt and pepper.

2   Add the chopped tomatoes, tomato purée and the kidney beans to the pan. Bring to the boil, lower the heat, and simmer, covered, for at least 40 minutes, stirring occasionally. Stir in the grated chocolate and cook for 3 minutes, or until melted.

3   Meanwhile, bring a large pan of lightly salted water to a rolling boil. Add the fusilli and cook according to the packet instructions, or until 'al dente'.

4   Drain the pasta, return to the pan and toss with the parsley. Tip into a warmed serving dish or spoon on to individual plates. Spoon the sauce over the pasta. Sprinkle with paprika and serve immediately with spoonfuls of soured cream.

✔ cows' milk-free   ✔ egg-free   ✔ gluten-free   ✔ wheat-free   ✔ nut-free   ✔ vegetarian   ✔ vegan   ✔ seafood-free

Spicy Cod Rice

Nutritional details

per 100 g

energy	127 kcals/533 kj
protein	10 g
carbohydrate	11 g
fat	5 g
fibre	1 g
sugar	0.8 g
sodium	0.3 g

EGG
FREE

Ingredients   Serves 4

1 tbsp plain flour
1 tbsp freshly chopped coriander
1 tsp ground cumin
1 tsp ground coriander
550 g/1¼ lb thick-cut cod fillet,
    skinned and cut
    into large chunks
4 tbsp groundnut oil
50 g/2 oz cashew nuts
1 bunch spring onions,
    trimmed and
    diagonally sliced
1 red chilli, deseeded
    and chopped
1 carrot, peeled and cut
    into matchsticks
125 g/4 oz frozen peas
450 g/1 lb cooked long-grain rice
2 tbsp sweet chilli sauce
2 tbsp soy sauce

Step-by-step guide

1   Mix together the flour, coriander, cumin and ground coriander on a large plate. Coat the cod in the spice mixture then place on a baking sheet, cover and chill in the refrigerator for 30 minutes.

2   Heat a large wok, then add 2 tablespoons of the oil and heat until almost smoking. Stir-fry the cashew nuts for 1 minute, until browned, then remove and reserve.

3   Add a further 1 tablespoon of the oil and heat until almost smoking. Add the cod and stir-fry for 2 minutes. Using a fish slice, turn the cod pieces over and cook for a further 2 minutes, until golden. Remove from the wok, place on a warm plate, cover and keep warm.

4   Add the remaining oil to the wok, heat until almost smoking, then stir-fry the spring onions and chilli for 1 minute before adding the carrots and peas and stir-frying for a further 2 minutes. Stir in the rice, chilli sauce, soy sauce and cashew nuts and stir-fry for 3 more minutes. Add the cod, heat for 1 minute, then serve immediately.

✓ cows' milk-free ✓ egg-free ✓ gluten-free ✓ wheat-free ✓ nut-free ✓ vegetarian ✓ vegan ✓ seafood-free

Spicy Mexican Chicken

Nutritional details

per 100 g

energy	129 kcals/540 kj
protein	12 g
carbohydrate	14 g
fat	3 g
fibre	1.5 g
sugar	1.7 g
sodium	0.2 g

Ingredients   Serves 4

2 tbsp olive oil
450 g/1 lb chicken mince
1 red onion, peeled
    and chopped
2 garlic cloves, peeled
    and chopped
1 red pepper, deseeded
    and chopped
1–2 tsp hot chilli powder
2 tbsp tomato purée
225 ml/8 fl oz chicken stock
salt and freshly ground
    black pepper
420 g can red kidney
    beans, drained
420 g can chilli beans, drained
350 g/12 oz spaghetti

To serve:
Monterey Jack or Cheddar
    cheese, grated
guacamole
hot chilli salsa

Step-by-step guide

1 Heat the oil in a large frying pan, add the chicken mince and cook for 5 minutes, stirring frequently with a wooden spoon to break up any lumps. Add the onion, garlic and pepper and cook for 3 minutes, stirring occasionally. Stir in the chilli powder and cook for a further 2 minutes.

2 Stir in the tomato purée, pour in the chicken stock and season to taste with salt and pepper. Bring to the boil, reduce the heat, and simmer, covered, for 20 minutes.

3 Add the kidney and chilli beans and cook, stirring occasionally, for 10 minutes, or until the chicken is tender.

4 Meanwhile, bring a large pan of lightly salted water to a rolling boil. Add the spaghetti and cook according to the packet instructions, or until 'al dente'.

5 Drain the spaghetti thoroughly, arrange on warmed plates and spoon over the chicken and bean mixture. Serve with grated cheese, guacamole and salsa.

✓ cows' milk-free   ✓ egg-free   ✓ gluten-free   ✓ wheat-free   ✓ nut-free   ✓ vegetarian   ✓ vegan   ✓ seafood-free

Stuffed Onions with Pine Nuts

Nutritional details

per 100 g

energy	86 kcals/358 kj
protein	4 g
carbohydrate	9 g
fat	4 g
fibre	1.3 g
sugar	6.4 g
sodium	0.2 g

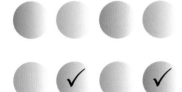

Ingredients   Serves 4

4 medium onions, peeled
2 garlic cloves, peeled and crushed
2 tbsp fresh brown breadcrumbs
2 tbsp white breadcrumbs
25 g/1 oz sultanas
25 g/1 oz pine nuts
50 g/2 oz low-fat hard cheese
　　such as Edam, grated
2 tbsp freshly chopped parsley
1 medium egg, beaten
salt and freshly ground
　　black pepper
salad leaves, to serve

Step-by-step guide

1 Preheat the oven to 200°C/400°F/ Gas Mark 6. Bring a pan of water to the boil, add the onions and cook gently for about 15 minutes.

2 Drain well. Allow the onions to cool, then slice each one in half horizontally.

3 Scoop out most of the onion flesh but leave a reasonably firm shell.

4 Chop up 4 tablespoons of the onion flesh and place in a bowl with the crushed garlic, breadcrumbs, sultanas, pine nuts, grated cheese and parsley.

5 Mix the breadcrumb mixture together thoroughly. Bind together with as much of the beaten egg as necessary to make a firm filling. Season to taste with salt and pepper.

6 Pile the mixture back into the onion shells and top with the grated cheese. Place on a oiled baking tray and cook in the preheated oven for 20–30 minutes or until golden brown. Serve immediately with the salad leaves.

✓ cows' milk-free ✓ egg-free ✓ gluten-free ✓ wheat-free ✓ nut-free ✓ vegetarian ✓ vegan ✓ seafood-free

Swede, Turnip, Parsnip & Potato Soup

Nutritional details

per 100 g

energy	126 kcals/526 kj
protein	2 g
carbohydrate	12 g
fat	8 g
fibre	1.6 g
sugar	3.5 g
sodium	0.3 g

Ingredients   Serves 4

2 large onions, peeled
25 g/1 oz butter
2 medium carrots,
    peeled and roughly chopped
175 g/6 oz swede,
    peeled and roughly chopped
125 g/4 oz turnip,
    peeled and roughly chopped
125 g/4 oz parsnips,
    peeled and roughly chopped
175 g/6 oz potatoes, peeled
1 litre/1¾ pints vegetable stock
½ tsp freshly grated nutmeg
salt and freshly ground black pepper
4 tbsp vegetable oil, for frying
125 ml/4 fl oz double cream
warm crusty bread, to serve

Step-by-step guide

1   Finely chop 1 onion. Melt the butter in a large saucepan and add the onion, carrots, swede, turnip, parsnip and potatoes. Cover and cook gently for about 10 minutes, without colouring. Stir occasionally during this time.

2   Add the stock and season to taste with the nutmeg, salt and pepper. Cover and bring to the boil, then reduce the heat and simmer gently for 15–20 minutes, or until the vegetables are tender. Remove from the heat and leave to cool for 30 minutes.

3   Heat the oil in a large, heavy-based frying pan. Add the onions and cook over a medium heat for about 2–3 minutes, stirring frequently until golden brown. Remove the onions with a slotted spoon and drain well on absorbent kitchen paper. As they cool, they will turn crispy.

4   Pour the cooled soup into a food processor or blender and process to form a smooth purée. Return to the cleaned pan, adjust the seasoning, then stir in the cream. Gently reheat and top with the crispy onions. Serve immediately with chunks of bread.

✓ cows' milk-free   ✓ egg-free   ✓ gluten-free   ✓ wheat-free   ✓ nut-free   ✓ vegetarian   ✓ vegan   ✓ seafood-free

Sweetcorn Fritters

Nutritional details

per 100 g

energy	174 kcals/730 kj
protein	4 g
carbohydrate	23 g
fat	8 g
fibre	1.3 g
sugar	5.7 g
sodium	0.3 g

Ingredients   Serves 4

4 tbsp sunflower oil
1 small onion, peeled and
    finely chopped
1 red chilli, deseeded and
    finely chopped
1 garlic clove, peeled and crushed
1 tsp ground coriander
325 g can sweetcorn
6 spring onions, trimmed
    and finely sliced
1 medium egg, lightly beaten
salt and freshly ground
    black pepper
3 tbsp plain flour
1 tsp baking powder
spring onion curls, to garnish

Step-by-step guide

1   Heat 1 tablespoon of the sunflower oil in a frying pan, add the onion and cook gently for 7–8 minutes or until beginning to soften. Add the chilli, garlic and ground coriander and cook for 1 minute, stirring continuously. Remove from the heat.

2   Drain the sweetcorn and tip into a mixing bowl. Lightly mash with a potato masher to break down the corn a little. Add the cooked onion mixture to the bowl with the spring onions and beaten egg. Season to taste with salt and pepper, then stir to mix together. Sift the flour and baking powder over the mixture and stir in.

3   Heat 2 tablespoons of the sunflower oil in a large frying pan. Drop 4 or 5 heaped teaspoonfuls of the sweetcorn mixture into the pan, and using a fish slice or spatula, flatten each to make a 1 cm/½ inch thick fritter.

4   Fry the fritters for 3 minutes, or until golden brown on the underside, turn over and fry for a further 3 minutes, or until cooked through and crisp.

5   Remove the fritters from the pan and drain on absorbent kitchen paper. Keep warm while cooking the remaining fritters, adding a little more oil if needed. Garnish with spring onion curls and serve immediately with a Thai-style chutney.

✓ cows' milk-free ✓ egg-free ✓ gluten-free ✓ wheat-free ✓ nut-free ✓ vegetarian ✓ vegan ✓ seafood-free

Vegetable Cassoulet

Nutritional details

per 100 g

energy	77 kcals/320 kj
protein	2 g
carbohydrate	10 g
fat	2.5 g
fibre	1.3 g
sugar	3.2 g
sodium	0.2 g

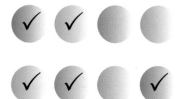

Ingredients   Serves 6

125 g/4 oz dried haricot beans,
    soaked overnight
2 tbsp olive oil
2 garlic cloves,
    peeled and chopped
225 g/8 oz baby onions,
    peeled and halved
2 carrots, peeled and diced
2 celery sticks, trimmed
    and finely chopped
1 red pepper,
    deseeded and chopped
175 g/6 oz mixed
    mushrooms, sliced
1 tbsp each freshly chopped
    rosemary, thyme and sage
150 ml/¼ pint red wine
4 tbsp tomato purée
1 tbsp dark soy sauce
salt and freshly ground
    black pepper
50 g/2 oz fresh breadcrumbs
1 tbsp freshly chopped parsley
basil sprigs, to garnish

Step-by-step guide

1   Preheat the oven to 190°C/375°F/
    Gas Mark 5. Drain the haricot
    beans and place in a saucepan with
    1.1 litres/2 pints of fresh water.
    Bring to the boil and boil rapidly
    for 10 minutes. Reduce the heat
    and simmer gently for 45 minutes.
    Drain the beans, reserving
    300 ml/½ pint of the liquid.

2   Heat 1 tablespoon of the oil in a
    flameproof casserole dish and add
    the garlic, onions, carrot, celery
    and red pepper. Cook for 10–12
    minutes until tender and starting
    to brown. Add a little water if the
    vegetables start to stick. Add the
    mushrooms and cook for a further
    5 minutes until softened. Add the
    herbs and stir briefly.

3   Stir in the red wine and boil
    rapidly for about 5 minutes until
    reduced and syrupy. Stir in the
    reserved beans and their liquid
    along with the tomato purée and
    soy sauce. Season to taste with
    salt and pepper.

4   Mix together the breadcrumbs
    and parsley with the remaining
    1 tablespoon of oil. Scatter this
    mixture evenly over the top of the
    stew. Cover loosely with foil and
    transfer to the preheated oven. Cook
    for 30 minutes. Carefully remove the
    foil and cook for a further 15–20
    minutes until the topping is crisp
    and golden. Serve immediately,
    garnished with basil sprigs.

✔ cows' milk-free ✔ egg-free ✔ gluten-free ✔ wheat-free ✔ nut-free ✔ vegetarian ✔ vegan ✔ seafood-free

Venetian-style Vegetables & Beans

Nutritional details

per 100 g

energy	74 kcals/308 kj
protein	2 g
carbohydrate	9 g
fat	3 g
fibre	1 g
sugar	3.4 g
sodium	trace

Ingredients   Serves 4

250 g/9 oz dried pinto beans
3 sprigs of fresh parsley
1 sprig of fresh rosemary
2 tbsp olive oil
200 g can chopped tomatoes
2 shallots, peeled

For the vegetable mixture:
1 large red onion, peeled
1 large white onion, peeled
1 medium carrot, peeled
2 sticks celery, trimmed
3 tbsp olive oil
3 bay leaves
1 tsp caster sugar
3 tbsp red wine vinegar
salt and freshly ground
    black pepper

Step-by-step guide

1 Put the beans in a bowl, cover with plenty of cold water and leave to soak for at least 8 hours, or overnight.

2 Drain and rinse the beans. Put in a large saucepan with 1.1 litres/ 2 pints cold water. Tie the parsley and rosemary in muslin and add to the beans with the olive oil. Boil rapidly for 10 minutes, then lower the heat and simmer for 20 minutes with the saucepan half covered. Stir in the tomatoes and shallots and simmer for a further 10–15 minutes, or until the beans are cooked.

3 Meanwhile, slice the red and white onion into rings and then finely dice the carrot and celery. Heat the olive oil in a saucepan and cook the onions over a very low heat for about 10 minutes. Add the carrot, celery and bay leaves to the saucepan and cook for a further 10 minutes, stirring frequently, until the vegetables are tender. Sprinkle with sugar, stir and cook for 1 minute.

4 Stir in the vinegar. Cook for 1 minute, then remove the saucepan from the heat. Drain the beans through a fine sieve, discarding all the herbs, then add the beans to the onion mixture and season well with salt and pepper. Mix gently, then tip the beans into a large serving bowl. Leave to cool, then serve at room temperature.

cows' milk-free ✓ egg-free ✓ gluten-free ✓ wheat-free ✓ nut-free ✓ vegetarian ✓ vegan ✓ seafood-free

White Bean Soup with Parmesan Croûtons

Nutritional details

per 100 g

energy	161 kcals/674 kj
protein	8 g
carbohydrate	19 g
fat	6 g
fibre	1 g
sugar	1.3 g
sodium	0.4 g

Ingredients   Serves 4

3 thick slices of white bread,
    cut into 1 cm/½ inch cubes
3 tbsp groundnut oil
2 tbsp Parmesan cheese, finely grated
1 tbsp light olive oil
1 large onion, peeled and
    finely chopped
50 g/2 oz unsmoked bacon lardons
    (or thick slices of bacon, diced)
1 tbsp fresh thyme leaves
2 x 400 g cannellini beans, drained
900 ml/1½ pints chicken stock
salt and freshly ground black pepper
1 tbsp prepared pesto sauce
50 g/2 oz piece of pepperoni
    sausage, diced
1 tbsp fresh lemon juice
1 tbsp fresh basil, roughly shredded

Step-by-step guide

1 Preheat the oven to 200°C/400°F/ Gas Mark 6. Place the cubes of bread in a bowl and pour over the groundnut oil. Stir to coat the bread, then sprinkle over the Parmesan cheese. Place on a lightly oiled baking tray and bake in the preheated oven for 10 minutes, or until crisp and golden.

2 Heat the olive oil in a large saucepan and cook the onion for 4–5 minutes until softened. Add the bacon and thyme and cook for a further 3 minutes. Stir in the beans, stock and black pepper and simmer gently for 5 minutes.

3 Place half the bean mixture and liquid into a food processor and blend until smooth.

4 Return the purée to the saucepan. Stir in the pesto sauce, pepperoni sausage and lemon juice and season to taste with salt and pepper.

5 Return the soup to the heat and cook for a further 2–3 minutes, or until piping hot. Place some of the beans in each serving bowl and add a ladleful of soup. Garnish with shredded basil and serve immediately with the croûtons scattered over the top.

✓ cows' milk-free   ✓ egg-free   ✓ gluten-free   ✓ wheat-free   ✓ nut-free   ✓ vegetarian   ✓ vegan   ✓ seafood-free

Wild Rice & Bacon Salad with Smoked Chicken

Nutritional details

per 100 g

energy	224 kcals/934 kj
protein	14 g
carbohydrate	6 g
fat	5 g
fibre	0.8 g
sugar	0.4 g
sodium	0.6 g

Ingredients   Serves 4

150 g/5 oz wild rice
50 g/2 oz pecan or walnut halves
1 tbsp vegetable oil
4 slices smoked bacon, diced
3–4 shallots, peeled and
    finely chopped
75 ml/3 fl oz walnut oil
2–3 tbsp sherry or cider vinegar
2 tbsp freshly chopped dill
salt and freshly ground
    black pepper
275 g/10 oz smoked chicken
    or duck breast, thinly sliced
dill sprigs, to garnish

Step-by-step guide

1   Put the wild rice in a medium saucepan with 600 ml/1 pint water and bring to the boil, stirring once or twice. Reduce the heat, cover and simmer gently for 30–50 minutes, depending on the texture you prefer, chewy or tender. Using a fork, gently fluff into a large bowl and leave to cool slightly.

2   Meanwhile, toast the nuts in a frying pan over a medium heat for 2 minutes, or until they are fragrant and lightly coloured, stirring and tossing frequently. Cool, then chop coarsely and add to the rice.

3   Heat the oil in the frying pan over a medium heat. Add the bacon and cook, stirring from time to time, for 3–4 minutes, or until crisp and brown. Remove from the pan and drain on absorbent kitchen paper. Add the shallots to the pan and cook for 4 minutes, or until just softened, stirring from time to time. Stir into the rice and nuts, with the drained bacon pieces.

4   Whisk the walnut oil, vinegar, half the dill and salt and pepper in a small bowl until combined. Pour the dressing over the rice mixture and toss well to combine. Mix the chicken and the remaining chopped dill into the rice, then spoon into bowls and garnish each serving with a dill sprig. Serve slightly warm, or at room temperature.

cows' milk-free   egg-free   gluten-free   wheat-free   nut-free   vegetarian   vegan   seafood-free

Coconut Rice Served with Stewed Ginger Fruits

Nutritional details

per 100 g

energy	181 kcals/753 kj
protein	2 g
carbohydrate	9 g
fat	12 g
fibre	0.6 g
sugar	6 g
sodium	trace

Ingredients   Serves 6–8

1 vanilla pod
450 ml/³⁄₄ pint coconut milk
1.1 litres/2 pints semi-skimmed milk
600 ml/1 pint double cream
100 g/3½ oz caster sugar
2 star anise
8 tbsp toasted desiccated coconut
250 g/9 oz short-grain pudding rice
1 tsp melted butter
2 mandarin oranges,
    peeled and pith removed
1 star fruit, sliced
50 g/2 oz stem ginger, finely diced
300 ml/½ pint sweet white wine
caster sugar, to taste

Step-by-step guide

1   Preheat the oven to 160°C/ 325°F/Gas Mark 3. Using a sharp knife, split the vanilla pod in half lengthways, scrape out the seeds from the pods and place both the pod and seeds in a large, heavy-based casserole dish. Pour in the coconut milk, the semi-skimmed milk and the double cream and stir in the sugar, star anise and 4 tablespoons of the toasted coconut. Bring to the boil, then simmer for 10 minutes, stirring occasionally. Remove the vanilla pod and star anise.

2   Wash the rice and add to the milk. Simmer gently for 25–30 minutes or until the rice is tender, stirring frequently. Stir in the melted butter.

3   Divide the mandarins into segments and place in a saucepan with the sliced star fruit and stem ginger. Pour in the white wine and 300 ml/½ pint water, bring to the boil, then reduce the heat and simmer for 20 minutes or until the liquid has reduced and the fruits softened. Add sugar to taste.

4   Serve the rice, topped with the stewed fruits and the remaining toasted coconut.

✓ cows' milk-free   ✓ egg-free   ✓ gluten-free   ✓ wheat-free   ✓ nut-free   ✓ vegetarian   ✓ vegan   ✓ seafood-free

Crunchy Rhubarb Crumble

Nutritional details

per 100 g

energy	172 kcals/724 kj
protein	4 g
carbohydrate	28 g
fat	5 g
fibre	1 g
sugar	17 g
sodium	trace

Ingredients   Serves 6

125 g/4 oz plain flour
50 g/2 oz softened butter
50 g/2 oz rolled oats
50 g/2 oz demerara sugar
1 tbsp sesame seeds
½ tsp ground cinnamon
450 g/1 lb fresh rhubarb
50 g/2 oz caster sugar
custard, to serve

Step-by-step guide

1 Preheat the oven to 180°C/350°F/ Gas Mark 4. Place the flour in a large bowl and cut the butter into cubes. Add to the flour and rub in with your fingertips until the mixture looks like fine breadcrumbs, or blend for a few seconds in a food processor.

2 Stir in the rolled oats, demerara sugar, sesame seeds and cinnamon. Mix well and reserve.

3 Prepare the rhubarb by removing the thick ends of the stalks and cut diagonally into 2.5 cm/1 inch chunks. Wash thoroughly and pat dry with a clean tea towel. Place the rhubarb in a 1.1 litre/2 pint pie dish.

4 Sprinkle the caster sugar over the rhubarb and top with the reserved

crumble mixture. Level the top of the crumble so that all the fruit is well covered and press down firmly. If liked, sprinkle the top with a little extra caster sugar.

5 Place on a baking sheet and bake in the preheated oven for 40–50 minutes, or until the fruit is soft and the topping is golden brown. Sprinkle the pudding with some more caster sugar and serve hot with custard.

✓ cows' milk-free ✓ egg-free ✓ gluten-free ✓ wheat-free ✓ nut-free ✓ vegetarian ✓ vegan ✓ seafood-free

Oaty Fruit Puddings

Nutritional details

per 100 g

energy	138 kcals/581 kj
protein	5 g
carbohydrate	23 g
fat	3 g
fibre	1.2 g
sugar	12 g
sodium	trace

Ingredients   Serves 4

125 g/4 oz rolled oats
50 g/2 oz butter, melted
2 tbsp chopped almonds
1 tbsp clear honey
pinch of ground cinnamon
2 pears, peeled, cored and
    finely chopped
1 tbsp marmalade
orange zest, to decorate
custard, to serve

Step-by-step guide

1 Preheat the oven to 200°C/400°F/ Gas Mark 6.

2 Lightly oil and line the bases of four individual pudding bowls or muffin tins with a small circle of greaseproof paper.

3 Mix together the oats, butter, nuts, honey and cinnamon in a small bowl.

4 Using a spoon, spread two thirds of the oaty mixture over the base and around the sides of the pudding bowls or muffin tins.

5 Toss together the pears and marmalade and spoon into the oaty cases.

6 Scatter over the remaining oaty mixture to cover the pears and marmalade.

7 Bake in the preheated oven for 15–20 minutes, until cooked and the tops of the puddings are golden and crisp.

8 Leave for 5 minutes before removing the pudding bowls or the muffin tins. Decorate with orange zest and serve hot with custard.

cows' milk-free   egg-free   gluten-free   wheat-free   nut-free   vegetarian   vegan   seafood-free

Poached Pears

Nutritional details

per 100 g

energy	96 kcals/403 kj
protein	0.8 g
carbohydrate	20 g
fat	1 g
fibre	1.1 g
sugar	17.7 g
sodium	trace

Ingredients   Serves 4

2 small cinnamon sticks
125 g/4 oz caster sugar
300 ml/½ pint red wine
150 ml/¼ pint water
thinly pared rind and juice of
    1 small orange
4 firm pears
orange slices, to decorate
frozen vanilla yogurt, or
    ice cream, to serve

Step-by-step guide

1 Place the cinnamon sticks on the work surface and with a rolling pin, slowly roll down the side of the cinnamon stick to bruise. Place in a large, heavy-based saucepan.

2 Add the sugar, wine, water, pared orange rind and juice to the pan and bring slowly to the boil, stirring occasionally until the sugar is dissolved.

3 Meanwhile peel the pears, leaving the stalks on.

4 Cut out the cores from the bottom of the pears and level them so that they stand upright.

5 Stand the pears in the syrup, cover the pan and simmer for 20 minutes or until tender.

6 Remove the pan from the heat and leave the pears to cool in the syrup, turning occasionally.

7 Arrange the pears on serving plates and spoon over the syrup. Decorate with the orange slices and serve with the yogurt or ice cream and any remaining juices.

Sweet-stewed Dried Fruits

Nutritional details

per 100 g

energy	139 kcals/592 kj
protein	1 g
carbohydrate	33 g
fat	1 g
fibre	2 g
sugar	26 g
sodium	trace

Ingredients   Serves 4

500 g/1 lb 2 oz packet mixed
     dried fruit salad
450 ml/³⁄₄ pint apple juice
2 tbsp clear honey
2 tbsp brandy
1 lemon
1 orange

To decorate:
crème fraîche
fine strips of pared orange rind

Step-by-step guide

1 Place the fruits, apple juice,
   clear honey and brandy in a
   small saucepan.

2 Using a small, sharp knife or a
   zester, carefully remove the zest
   from the lemon and orange and
   place in the pan.

3 Squeeze the juice from the lemon
   and oranges and add to the pan.

4 Bring the fruit mixture to the boil
   and simmer for about 1 minute.
   Remove the pan from the heat and
   allow the mixture to cool completely.

5 Transfer the mixture to a large
   bowl, cover with clingfilm and

chill in the refrigerator overnight
to allow the flavours to blend.

6 Spoon the stewed fruit into
   four shallow dessert dishes.
   Decorate with a large spoonful
   of crème fraîche and a few
   strips of the pared orange
   rind and serve.

✓ cows' milk-free ✓ egg-free ✓ gluten-free ✓ wheat-free ✓ nut-free ✓ vegetarian ✓ vegan ✓ seafood-free